More Mental Maths Tests

for ages 9–10

✓ **Ten complete Mental Maths timed tests, together with a pre-recorded CD**

✓ **Ideal practice for National Tests**

✓ **Bonus material includes record sheets and addition squares**

Introduction

Our Mental Maths Tests were originally devised to provide practice for the optional tests for Years 3, 4 and 5 taking place in May using the same test materials each year. The materials in this book provide practice for the type of questions that appear in those tests but also for other aspects of mathematics at the appropriate levels indicated by the Framework for Teaching Mathematics.

Many teachers have found that our tests provide a very useful structure for consolidation lessons. By working through the tests with the pupils, teachers can gain valuable insights into their pupils' levels of performance. At the same time the children are gaining experience of working in a test situation, listening to recorded questions that are timed in the same way as the 'real' test.

General instructions for the administration of the tests

To make these tests seem as realistic as possible children should have clear desks and only a pen or pencil to write with. They should not be supplied with paper for working out the answers.

Before starting each test the children should write their name and school in the spaces provided.

Inform the children that:

- they should work individually and should not talk at all during the test;

- there will be 20 questions altogether;

- they will be allowed 5 seconds to answer each of the first five questions, 10 seconds for each of the next ten questions and 15 seconds for each of the last five questions;

- for some questions, some information will be provided on the test sheet;

- calculators or other equipment are not allowed;

- they should not rub out answers but, if they wish to change them, they can cross them out and write their new answers next to the incorrect ones;

- if they cannot do a question they should put a cross in the answer box.

Andrew Brodie: More Mental Maths Tests 9–10 © A & C Black

Test 1

Before playing the test on the CD give each child a copy of the test and read out the following script:

> **Listen to the instructions carefully. I will answer any questions that you have after I have finished reading the instructions to you. Once the test starts you will not be able to ask any questions.**
>
> **The first question is a practice question. In the test there will then be twenty questions.**
>
> **Each question has an answer box. Make sure that you only write the answer to the correct question in the box. Try to work out each answer in your head. You can make notes outside the answer box if this helps you but do not try to write out calculations because you will not have enough time. For some questions you will find important information already provided for you.**
>
> **Each question will be read out twice. Listen carefully then work out your answer. If you cannot do the question, just put a cross. If you make a mistake, do not rub out the wrong answer; cross it out and write the correct answer.**
>
> **Some questions are easy and some are more difficult. Do not worry if you find a question hard; just do your best. I hope that you enjoy the test.**

At this point, answer any questions that the children ask.

> **Now listen carefully to the practice question. You will hear the question twice, then you will have five seconds to work out and write down the answer.**
>
> *What is five add two?*
>
> *What is five add two?*

Allow the children five seconds to write the answer, then say:

> **Put your pencil down.**

Check that the children have written the answer to the practice question in the practice question answer box. Remind them that they cannot ask any more questions once the test is started. When you are ready press start on your CD player.

When the test is finished ask the children to stop writing then collect the test sheets. For ease of marking we have created a copy of the test paper with the answers entered in the appropriate boxes.

Questions for Test 1

For each of the first ten questions you have five seconds to work out and write down the answer.

1 What must be added to fourteen to make sixty?

2 What is the product of six and seven?

3 Write the fraction one half as a decimal.

4 Add twenty to eighty-seven.

5 Divide seventy-two by nine.

For each of the next questions you have ten seconds to work out and write down the answer.

6 Look at your answer sheet. The clock shows the time my favourite programme starts in the evening. Write the time using 24-hour clock notation.

7 Double zero point four five.

8 Write one quarter of a litre in millilitres.

9 Subtract three thousand nine hundred and ninety-nine from six thousand.

10 Multiply eighty-two by one hundred.

11 What number is ninety-nine less than two hundred and eighteen?

12 How much money is ten percent of forty-five pounds?

13 In a survey six out of ten people said they preferred tea to coffee. What percentage is that?

14 What is my change from five pounds when I spend one pound eighty pence?

15 My book weighs two point one kilograms. How many grams does my book weigh?

For each of the next five questions you have fifteen seconds to work out and write down the answer.

16 Look at your answer sheet. What is the perimeter of the rectangle?

17 I save one pound forty pence each week. How much money do I have after four weeks?

18 Add four point five to two point nine.

19 I counted the chocolate buttons in each of five packets. My results are shown on the answer sheet. What is the mode of this data?

20 Three pounds forty pence is shared between two people. How much money does each person have?

Put your pencil down. The test is over.

Andrew Brodie: More Mental Maths Tests 9–10 © A & C Black

Test 1

First name _____ Last name _____

School _____

_____ **Total marks** [ ]

Practice question

[|]

Five-second questions

1		14
2		
3		$\frac{1}{2}$
4		87
5		

Ten-second questions

| 6 | |

7		0.45
8	ml	$\frac{1}{4}$ l
9		3999
10		

11		218
12	£	
13		%
14	£	£1.80
15		g	2.1 kg

Fifteen-second questions

| 16 | cm | 2.5 cm / 4 cm |

17	£	
18		4.5 2.9
19		21 20 22 20 20
20	£	

Practice question

	7

Five-second questions

1	46	14

2	42

3	0.5	$\frac{1}{2}$

4	107	87

5	8

Ten-second questions

6	20.00	

7	0.9	0.45

8	250 ml	$\frac{1}{4}$ l

9	2001	3999

10	8200

11	119	218

12	£4.50

13	60%

14	£3.20	£1.80

15	2100g	2.1 kg

Fifteen-second questions

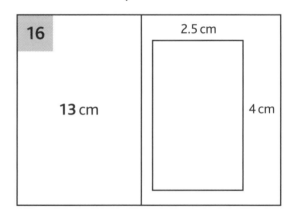

16	13 cm	2.5 cm	4 cm

17	£5.60

18	7.4	4.5 2.9

19	20	21 20 22 20 20

20	£1.70

Andrew Brodie: More Mental Maths Tests 9–10 © A & C Black

Test 2

Before playing the test on the CD give each child a copy of the test and read out the following script:

> **Listen to the instructions carefully. I will answer any questions that you have after I have finished reading the instructions to you. Once the test starts you will not be able to ask any questions.**
>
> **The first question is a practice question. In the test there will then be twenty questions.**
>
> **Each question has an answer box. Make sure that you only write the answer to the correct question in the box. Try to work out each answer in your head. You can make notes outside the answer box if this helps you but do not try to write out calculations because you will not have enough time. For some questions you will find important information already provided for you.**
>
> **Each question will be read out twice. Listen carefully then work out your answer. If you cannot do the question, just put a cross. If you make a mistake, do not rub out the wrong answer; cross it out and write the correct answer.**
>
> **Some questions are easy and some are more difficult. Do not worry if you find a question hard; just do your best. I hope that you enjoy the test.**

At this point, answer any questions that the children ask.

> **Now listen carefully to the practice question. You will hear the question twice, then you will have five seconds to work out and write down the answer..**
>
> > *What is six minus four?*
> >
> > *What is six minus four?*

Allow the children five seconds to write the answer, then say:

> **Put your pencil down.**

Check that the children have written the answer to the practice question in the practice question answer box. Remind them that they cannot ask any more questions once the test is started. When you are ready press start on your CD player.

When the test is finished ask the children to stop writing then collect the test sheets. For ease of marking we have created a copy of the test paper with the answers entered in the appropriate boxes.

Questions for Test 2

For each of the first ten questions you have five seconds to work out and write down the answer.

1   Write one quarter as a decimal.

2   Multiply seven by nine.

3   Fifty-eight subtract sixteen.

4   What is four hundred and fifty times ten?

5   Divide forty-eight by six.

For each of the next questions you have ten seconds to work out and write down the answer.

6   Multiply three point four by ten.

7   What weight is one tenth of four kilograms?

8   Look at your answer sheet. The clock shows the time my favourite programme ends in the evening. Write the time using 24-hour clock notation.

9   Write three point five litres in millilitres.

10   The answer sheet shows the month of July on a page from a calendar. What day of the week was the first of August?

11   Sixty-eight percent of children in a school travel to school by car. What percentage do not travel to school by car?

12   How much money is ten percent of seventy-five pounds?

13   Subtract two thousand four hundred and ninety-nine from three thousand.

14   Multiply twenty-seven by four.

15   Add forty-nine to two hundred and seventy.

For each of the next five questions you have fifteen seconds to work out and write down the answer.

16   Look at your answer sheet. What is the perimeter of the equilateral triangle?

17   Add two point eight to one point seven.

18   Kim has a spelling test every week for six weeks. Her results are shown on the answer sheet. What is the mode of this data?

19   Six pounds seventy-five pence is shared equally between three people. How much money does each person have?

20   What is my change from ten pounds when I spend six pounds forty-two pence?

Put your pencil down. The test is over.

Andrew Brodie: More Mental Maths Tests 9–10 © A & C Black

Test 2

First name _____   Last name _____

School _____

_____   **Total marks** [ ]

Practice question

[ ]

Five-second questions

| 1 | | $\frac{1}{4}$ |

| 2 | |

| 3 | | 58   16 |

| 4 | | 450 |

| 5 | | 48 |

Ten-second questions

| 6 | | 3.4 |

| 7 | g | 4 kg |

| 8 | | 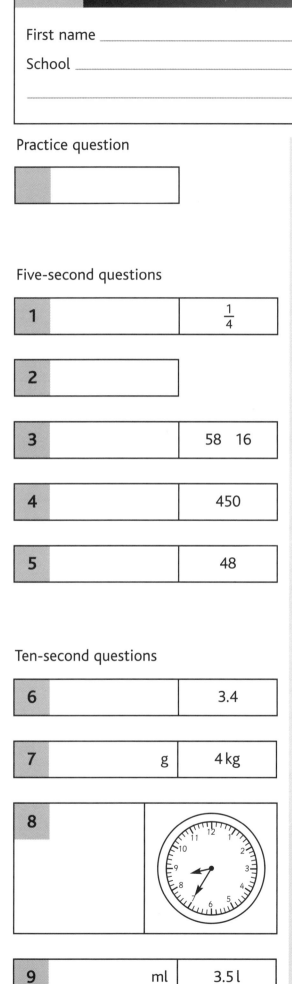 |

| 9 | ml | 3.5 l |

| 10 | |

		JULY			
Monday		6	13	20	27
Tuesday		7	14	21	28
Wednesday	1	8	15	22	29
Thursday	2	9	16	23	30
Friday	3	10	17	24	31
Saturday	4	11	18	25	
Sunday	5	12	19	26	

| 11 | % | 68% |

| 12 | £ | £75 |

| 13 | | 2499 |

| 14 | |

| 15 | | 49   270 |

Fifteen-second questions

| 16 | cm | △ 2.5 cm |

| 17 | | 2.8   1.7 |

| 18 | | 10 9 7 9 8 9 |

| 19 | £ | £6.75 |

| 20 | £ | £6.42 |

Practice question

	2

Five-second questions

1	0.25	$\frac{1}{4}$

2	63

3	42	58 16

4	4500	450

5	8	48

Ten-second questions

6	34	3.4

7	400 g	4 kg

8	20.35	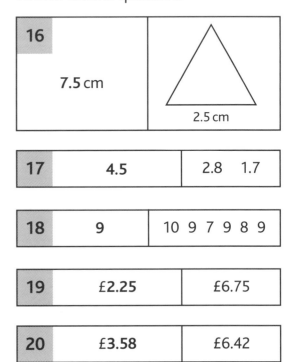

9	3500 ml	3.5 l

10	**Saturday**			
	JULY			
Monday	6	13	20	27
Tuesday	7	14	21	28
Wednesday	1	8	15	22	29
Thursday	2	9	16	23	30
Friday	3	10	17	24	31
Saturday	4	11	18	25
Sunday	5	12	19	26

11	32%	68%

12	£7.50	£75

13	501	2499

14	108

15	319	49 270

Fifteen-second questions

16	7.5 cm	2.5 cm

17	4.5	2.8 1.7

18	9	10 9 7 9 8 9

19	£2.25	£6.75

20	£3.58	£6.42

Test 3

Before playing the test on the CD give each child a copy of the test and read out the following script:

> **Listen to the instructions carefully. I will answer any questions that you have after I have finished reading the instructions to you. Once the test starts you will not be able to ask any questions.**
>
> **The first question is a practice question. In the test there will then be twenty questions.**
>
> **Each question has an answer box. Make sure that you only write the answer to the correct question in the box. Try to work out each answer in your head. You can make notes outside the answer box if this helps you but do not try to write out calculations because you will not have enough time. For some questions you will find important information already provided for you.**
>
> **Each question will be read out twice. Listen carefully then work out your answer. If you cannot do the question, just put a cross. If you make a mistake, do not rub out the wrong answer; cross it out and write the correct answer.**
>
> **Some questions are easy and some are more difficult. Do not worry if you find a question hard; just do your best. I hope that you enjoy the test.**

At this point, answer any questions that the children ask.

> **Now listen carefully to the practice question. You will hear the question twice, then you will have five seconds to work out and write down the answer.**
>
> > *What is seven add four?*
> >
> > *What is seven add four?*

Allow the children five seconds to write the answer, then say:

> **Put your pencil down.**

Check that the children have written the answer to the practice question in the practice question answer box. Remind them that they cannot ask any more questions once the test is started. When you are ready press start on your CD player.

When the test is finished ask the children to stop writing then collect the test sheets. For ease of marking we have created a copy of the test paper with the answers entered in the appropriate boxes.

For each of the first ten questions you have five seconds to work out and write down the answer.

1   Write the fraction three quarters as a decimal.

2   What is the difference between eighteen and twenty-five?

3   Eight times five.

4   Add forty to ninety-eight.

5   Share thirty-six equally between four.

For each of the next questions you have ten seconds to work out and write down the answer.

6   What is ten percent of ninety pounds?

7   The answer sheet shows the month of May on a page from a calendar. What day of the week was the thirtieth of April?

8   Write three quarters of a litre in millilitres.

9   Increase three hundred and eighty by forty-five.

10   Look at your answer sheet. What is the perimeter of the square?

11   Look at your answer sheet. The clock shows the time I get up in the morning. Write the time using twenty-four hour clock notation.

12   Add one thousand and one to two thousand nine hundred and ninety nine.

13   What is the total of two point five, three and one?

14   What is the product of five point two and ten?

15   Subtract one point two from three point nine.

For each of the next five questions you have fifteen seconds to work out and write down the answer.

16   Look at your answer sheet. Draw a ring around the number that is not a factor of twelve.

17   What is twenty-five percent of six hundred pounds?

18   Look at your answer sheet. What is the perimeter of the rectangle?

19   I save two pounds fifty pence each week. How much money do I have after five weeks?

20   How much change do I have from twenty pounds when I spend eight pounds thirty pence?

Put your pencil down. The test is over.

Test 3

First name _____   Last name _____

School _____

_____   **Total marks** [   ]

Practice question

[   ]

Five-second questions

| 1 | | $\frac{3}{4}$ |

| 2 | | 18   25 |

| 3 | | |

| 4 | | 98 |

| 5 | | 36 |

Ten-second questions

| 6 | £ | £90 |

7

	MAY			
Monday	4	11	18	25
Tuesday	5	12	19	26
Wednesday	6	13	20	27
Thursday	7	14	21	28
Friday	1	8	15	22	29
Saturday	2	9	16	23	30
Sunday	3	10	17	24	31

| 8 | ml | $\frac{3}{4}$ l |

| 9 | | 380 |

10   cm   [ ] 3.5 cm

11
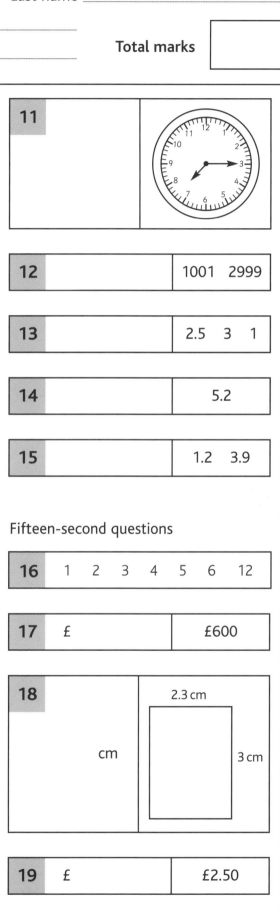

| 12 | | 1001   2999 |

| 13 | | 2.5   3   1 |

| 14 | | 5.2 |

| 15 | | 1.2   3.9 |

Fifteen-second questions

| 16 | 1   2   3   4   5   6   12 |

| 17 | £ | £600 |

18   cm   [2.3 cm × 3 cm rectangle]

| 19 | £ | £2.50 |

| 20 | £ | £8.30 |

Practice question

11

Five-second questions

1	0.75	$\frac{3}{4}$

2	7	18 25

3	40

4	138	98

5	9	36

Ten-second questions

6	£9	£90

7	Thursday

	MAY				
Monday		4	11	18	25
Tuesday		5	12	19	26
Wednesday		6	13	20	27
Thursday		7	14	21	28
Friday	1	8	15	22	29
Saturday	2	9	16	23	30
Sunday	3	10	17	24	31

8	750 ml	$\frac{3}{4}$ l

9	425	380

10	14 cm	3.5 cm

11	07.15

12	4000	1001 2999

13	6.5	2.5 3 1

14	52	5.2

15	2.7	1.2 3.9

Fifteen-second questions

16	1 2 3 4 ⑤ 6 12

17	£150	£600

18	10.6 cm	2.3 cm / 3 cm

19	£12.50	£2.50

20	£11.70	£8.30

Test 4

Before playing the test on the CD give each child a copy of the test and read out the following script:

> **Listen to the instructions carefully. I will answer any questions that you have after I have finished reading the instructions to you. Once the test starts you will not be able to ask any questions.**
>
> **The first question is a practice question. In the test there will then be twenty questions.**
>
> **Each question has an answer box. Make sure that you only write the answer to the correct question in the box. Try to work out each answer in your head. You can make notes outside the answer box if this helps you but do not try to write out calculations because you will not have enough time. For some questions you will find important information already provided for you.**
>
> **Each question will be read out twice. Listen carefully then work out your answer. If you cannot do the question, just put a cross. If you make a mistake, do not rub out the wrong answer; cross it out and write the correct answer.**
>
> **Some questions are easy and some are more difficult. Do not worry if you find a question hard; just do your best. I hope that you enjoy the test.**

At this point, answer any questions that the children ask.

> **Now listen carefully to the practice question. You will hear the question twice, then you will have five seconds to work out and write down the answer.**
>
> > *What is eight take away three?*
> >
> > *What is eight take away three?*

Allow the children five seconds to write the answer, then say:

> **Put your pencil down.**

Check that the children have written the answer to the practice question in the practice question answer box. Remind them that they cannot ask any more questions once the test is started. When you are ready press start on your CD player.

When the test is finished ask the children to stop writing then collect the test sheets. For ease of marking we have created a copy of the test paper with the answers entered in the appropriate boxes.

For each of the first ten questions you have five seconds to work out and write down the answer.

1   Thirteen minus eight.

2   What is three times twenty?

3   Multiply fourteen point four by ten.

4   Share twenty-seven between three.

5   Double eighteen.

For each of the next questions you have ten seconds to work out and write down the answer.

6   What is half of four point eight?

7   What is the difference between six thousand and four thousand eight hundred?

8   Look at your answer sheet. The clock shows the time a school is unlocked in the morning. Write the time using twenty-four hour clock notation.

9   Multiply forty by one hundred.

10   How many millilitres are there in one and a half litres?

11   Subtract two point four from five point seven.

12   What is ten percent of forty-five pounds?

13   What is the sum of seventeen and four point six?

14   Add eighty-five to two hundred and eighty.

15   The answer sheet shows the month of October on a page from a calendar. What day of the week was the second of November?

For each of the next five questions you have fifteen seconds to work out and write down the answer.

16   Look at your answer sheet. Draw a ring around the number that is not a factor of sixteen.

17   How much more is seven thousand and one than two thousand nine hundred and ninety-nine?

18   Look at your answer sheet. What is the perimeter of the equilateral triangle?

19   Share eleven pounds between four people.

20   How many vertices does a cube have?

Put your pencil down. The test is over.

First name _____ Last name _____

School _____

_____

Total marks

Practice question

Five-second questions

1	

2	

3	14.4

4	27

5	18

Ten-second questions

6	4.8

7	4800

8	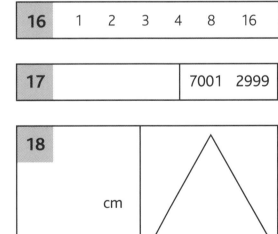

9	

10	ml	$1\frac{1}{2}$ l

11	2.4 5.7

12	£	£45

13	17 4.6

14	85 280

15	

	OCTOBER			
Monday	5	12	19	26
Tuesday	6	13	20	27
Wednesday	7	14	21	28
Thursday	1	8	15	22	29
Friday	2	9	16	23	30
Saturday	3	10	17	24	31
Sunday	4	11	18	25

Fifteen-second questions

16	1 2 3 4 8 16

17	7001 2999

18	cm	

3.2 cm

19	£	£11

20	

Practice question

5

Five-second questions

1	5

2	60

3	144	14.4

4	9	27

5	36	18

Ten-second questions

6	2.4	4.8

7	1200	4800

8	06.45	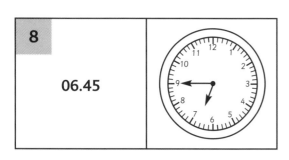

9	4000

10	1500 ml	$1\frac{1}{2}$ l

11	3.3	2.4 5.7

12	£4.50	£45

13	21.6	17 4.6

14	365	85 280

15	**Monday**

	OCTOBER			
Monday	5	12	19	26
Tuesday	6	13	20	27
Wednesday	7	14	21	28
Thursday	1	8	15	22	29
Friday	2	9	16	23	30
Saturday	3	10	17	24	31
Sunday	4	11	18	25

Fifteen-second questions

16	1 2 ③ 4 8 16

17	4002	7001 2999

18	9.6 cm	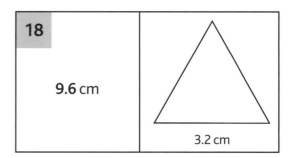 3.2 cm

19	£2.75	£11

20	8

Test 5

Before playing the test on the CD give each child a copy of the test and read out the following script:

> **Listen to the instructions carefully. I will answer any questions that you have after I have finished reading the instructions to you. Once the test starts you will not be able to ask any questions.**
>
> **The first question is a practice question. In the test there will then be twenty questions.**
>
> **Each question has an answer box. Make sure that you only write the answer to the correct question in the box. Try to work out each answer in your head. You can make notes outside the answer box if this helps you but do not try to write out calculations because you will not have enough time. For some questions you will find important information already provided for you.**
>
> **Each question will be read out twice. Listen carefully then work out your answer. If you cannot do the question, just put a cross. If you make a mistake, do not rub out the wrong answer; cross it out and write the correct answer.**
>
> **Some questions are easy and some are more difficult. Do not worry if you find a question hard; just do your best. I hope that you enjoy the test.**

At this point, answer any questions that the children ask.

> **Now listen carefully to the practice question. You will hear the question twice, then you will have five seconds to work out and write down the answer.**
>
> *What is three add five?*
>
> *What is three add five?*

Allow the children five seconds to write the answer, then say:

> **Put your pencil down.**

Check that the children have written the answer to the practice question in the practice question answer box. Remind them that they cannot ask any more questions once the test is started. When you are ready press start on your CD player.

When the test is finished ask the children to stop writing then collect the test sheets. For ease of marking we have created a copy of the test paper with the answers entered in the appropriate boxes.

For each of the first ten questions you have five seconds to work out and write down the answer.

1   Write the fraction three tenths as a decimal.

2   What is the product of six and nine?

3   Double thirty-five.

4   Subtract twenty-eight from one hundred.

5   Divide forty by five.

For each of the next questions you have ten seconds to work out and write down the answer.

6   Multiply twenty-five by six.

7   What is half of six point four?

8   Look at your answer sheet. The clock shows the time a school is locked in the evening. Write the time using twenty-four hour clock notation.

9   A regular heptagon has sides of four centimetres. What is its perimeter?

10   Write two and a half kilograms in grams.

11   Look at your answer sheet. Write the missing number in the sequence.

12   Six point eight minus three point five.

13   How much money is twenty percent of twenty pounds?

14   Add four point six to three point four.

15   The answer sheet shows the month of June on a page from a calendar. What day of the week was the third of July?

For each of the next five questions you have fifteen seconds to work out and write down the answer.

16   Look at your answer sheet. Draw a ring around the number that is not a factor of twenty.

17   What is twenty-five percent of nine hundred pounds?

18   Subtract three thousand nine hundred and ninety from nine thousand and four.

19   Share eight pounds between five people.

20   What is three times four times five?

Put your pencil down. The test is over.

First name _____   Last name _____

School _____

_____

Total marks

Practice question

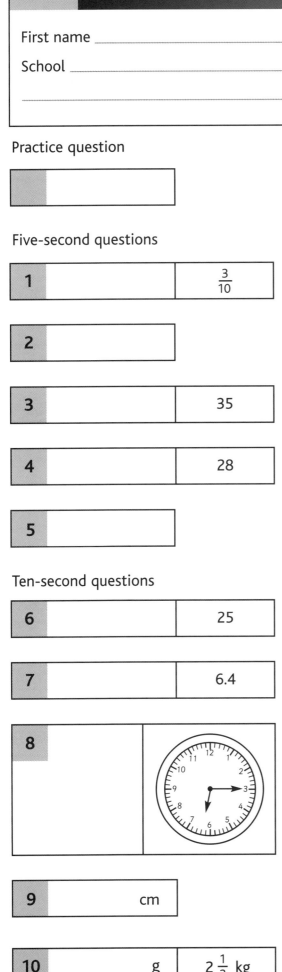

Five-second questions

| 1 | | $\frac{3}{10}$ |

| 2 | |

| 3 | | 35 |

| 4 | | 28 |

| 5 | |

Ten-second questions

| 6 | | 25 |

| 7 | | 6.4 |

| 8 | |

| 9 | cm |

| 10 | g | $2\frac{1}{2}$ kg |

| 11 | ... 7 11 15 | | 23 27 ... |

| 12 | | 6.8   3.5 |

| 13 | £ | 20% |

| 14 | | 4.6   3.4 |

| 15 | |

	JUNE			
Monday	1	8	15	22	29
Tuesday	2	9	16	23	30
Wednesday	3	10	17	24	
Thursday	4	11	18	25	
Friday	5	12	19	26	
Saturday	6	13	20	27	
Sunday	7	14	21	28	

Fifteen-second questions

| 16 | 1 2 4 5 8 10 20 |

| 17 | £ | £900 |

| 18 | | 3990 9004 |

| 19 | £ | £8 |

| 20 | |

Practice question

	8

Five-second questions

1	0.3	$\frac{3}{10}$

2	54

3	70	35

4	72	28

5	8

Ten-second questions

6	150	25

7	3.2	6.4

8	18.15	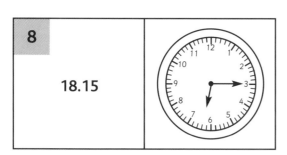

9	28 cm

10	2500 g	$2\frac{1}{2}$ kg

11	... 7 11 15 **19** 23 27 ...

12	3.3	6.8 3.5

13	£4	20%

14	8	4.6 3.4

15	**Friday**

	JUNE				
Monday	1	8	15	22	29
Tuesday	2	9	16	23	30
Wednesday	3	10	17	24	
Thursday	4	11	18	25	
Friday	5	12	19	26	
Saturday	6	13	20	27	
Sunday	7	14	21	28	

Fifteen-second questions

16	1 2 4 5 (8) 10 20

17	£225	£900

18	5014	3990 9004

19	£1.60	£8

20	60

   Andrew Brodie: More Mental Maths Tests 9–10 © A & C Black

Test 6

Before playing the test on the CD give each child a copy of the test and read out the following script:

Listen to the instructions carefully. I will answer any questions that you have after I have finished reading the instructions to you. Once the test starts you will not be able to ask any questions.

The first question is a practice question. In the test there will then be twenty questions.

Each question has an answer box. Make sure that you only write the answer to the correct question in the box. Try to work out each answer in your head. You can make notes outside the answer box if this helps you but do not try to write out calculations because you will not have enough time. For some questions you will find important information already provided for you.

Each question will be read out twice. Listen carefully then work out your answer. If you cannot do the question, just put a cross. If you make a mistake, do not rub out the wrong answer; cross it out and write the correct answer.

Some questions are easy and some are more difficult. Do not worry if you find a question hard; just do your best. I hope that you enjoy the test.

At this point, answer any questions that the children ask.

Now listen carefully to the practice question. You will hear the question twice, then you will have five seconds to work out and write down the answer.

What is half of eight?

What is half of eight?

Allow the children five seconds to write the answer, then say:

Put your pencil down.

Check that the children have written the answer to the practice question in the practice question answer box. Remind them that they cannot ask any more questions once the test is started. When you are ready press start on your CD player.

When the test is finished ask the children to stop writing then collect the test sheets. For ease of marking we have created a copy of the test paper with the answers entered in the appropriate boxes.

Questions for Test 6

For each of the first ten questions you have five seconds to work out and write down the answer.

1 Double four point two.

2 Add seven to forty-eight.

3 Divide seventy-two by eight.

4 Write the fraction nine tenths as a decimal.

5 Forty minus eighteen.

For each of the next questions you have ten seconds to work out and write down the answer.

6 Add one thousand and three to two thousand nine hundred and ninety eight.

7 Subtract one point eight from seven.

8 Look at your answer sheet. The clock shows the time a train leaves a station one evening. Write the time using twenty-four hour clock notation.

9 Write four and a quarter metres in centimetres.

10 Multiply twenty-five by seven.

11 Add sixty-eight to forty-nine.

12 Look at your answer sheet. Write the missing number in the sequence.

13 What is ten percent of ninety-five pounds?

14 What is three tenths of fifty?

15 The answer sheet shows the month of December on a page from a calendar. What day of the week was the twenty-ninth of November?

For each of the next five questions you have fifteen seconds to work out and write down the answer.

16 Look at your answer sheet. Draw a ring around the number that is not a factor of eighteen.

17 Look at your answer sheet. What is the area of the rectangle?

18 Alex has a spelling test every week for six weeks. His results are shown on the answer sheet. What is the mode of this data?

19 Share nine pounds between four people.

20 What is half of half of twenty?

Put your pencil down. The test is over.

Andrew Brodie: More Mental Maths Tests 9–10 © A & C Black

Test 6

First name _____ Last name _____

School _____

Total marks ____

Practice question

Five-second questions

1		4.2

2		48

3		72

4		$\frac{9}{10}$

5	

Ten-second questions

6		1003 2998

7		1.8

8		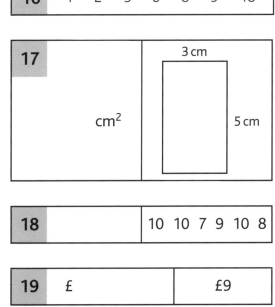

9	cm	$4\frac{1}{4}$ m

10	

11		68 49

12	... 29 32 35		41 44 ...

13	£	£95

14		$\frac{3}{10}$

15	

DECEMBER

Monday		7	14	21	28
Tuesday	1	8	15	22	29
Wednesday	2	9	16	23	30
Thursday	3	10	17	24	31
Friday	4	11	18	25
Saturday	5	12	19	26
Sunday	6	13	20	27

Fifteen-second questions

16	1 2 3 6 8 9 18

17	cm²	3 cm / 5 cm

18		10 10 7 9 10 8

19	£	£9

20	

Practice question

	4

Five-second questions

1	8.4	4.2

2	55	48

3	9	72

4	0.9	$\frac{9}{10}$

5	22

Ten-second questions

6	4001	1003 2998

7	5.2	1.8

8	21.25	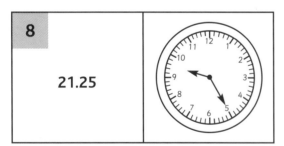

9	425 cm	$4\frac{1}{4}$ m

10	175

11	117	68 49

12	... 29 32 35	**38**	41 44 ...

13	£9.50	£95

14	15	$\frac{3}{10}$

15	**Sunday**

	DECEMBER				
Monday		7	14	21	28
Tuesday	1	8	15	22	29
Wednesday	2	9	16	23	30
Thursday	3	10	17	24	31
Friday	4	11	18	25	
Saturday	5	12	19	26	
Sunday	6	13	20	27	

Fifteen-second questions

16	1 2 3 6 (8) 9 18

17	15 cm²	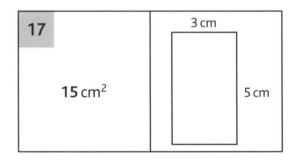

3 cm
5 cm

18	10	10 10 7 9 10 8

19	£2.25	£9

20	5

Test 7

Before playing the test on the CD give each child a copy of the test and read out the following script:

> **Listen to the instructions carefully. I will answer any questions that you have after I have finished reading the instructions to you. Once the test starts you will not be able to ask any questions.**
>
> **The first question is a practice question. In the test there will then be twenty questions.**
>
> **Each question has an answer box. Make sure that you only write the answer to the correct question in the box. Try to work out each answer in your head. You can make notes outside the answer box if this helps you but do not try to write out calculations because you will not have enough time. For some questions you will find important information already provided for you.**
>
> **Each question will be read out twice. Listen carefully then work out your answer. If you cannot do the question, just put a cross. If you make a mistake, do not rub out the wrong answer; cross it out and write the correct answer.**
>
> **Some questions are easy and some are more difficult. Do not worry if you find a question hard; just do your best. I hope that you enjoy the test.**

At this point, answer any questions that the children ask.

> **Now listen carefully to the practice question. You will hear the question twice, then you will have five seconds to work out and write down the answer.**
>
> > **What is two times four?**
> >
> > **What is two times four?**

Allow the children five seconds to write the answer, then say:

> **Put your pencil down.**

Check that the children have written the answer to the practice question in the practice question answer box. Remind them that they cannot ask any more questions once the test is started. When you are ready press start on your CD player.

When the test is finished ask the children to stop writing then collect the test sheets. For ease of marking we have created a copy of the test paper with the answers entered in the appropriate boxes.

Questions for Test 7

For each of the first ten questions you have five seconds to work out and write down the answer.

1   Write the fraction seven tenths as a decimal.

2   What is six times seven?

3   Subtract forty-two from one hundred.

4   Add seven to twenty-nine.

5   Divide thirty-five by seven.

For each of the next questions you have ten seconds to work out and write down the answer.

6   Add twenty-eight to eighty-two.

7   Subtract three point four from six.

8   Look at your answer sheet. The clock shows the time a bus arrives one evening. Write the time using twenty-four hour clock notation.

9   Subtract two thousand nine hundred from eight thousand four hundred.

10   Multiply twenty-five by nine.

11   Multiply six point four by one hundred.

12   Look at your answer sheet. Write the missing number in the sequence.

13   What is twenty percent of thirty-five pounds?

14   Double six point nine.

15   The answer sheet shows the month of January on a page from a calendar. What day of the week was the third of February?

For each of the next five questions you have fifteen seconds to work out and write down the answer.

16   Look at your answer sheet. Draw a ring around the number that is not a factor of twenty-four.

17   Look at your answer sheet. What is the area of the rectangle?

18   I save one pound seventy-five pence every week. How much money do I have after four weeks?

19   How much change do I have from twenty pounds when I spend three pounds forty pence?

20   What is the answer when the double of eight is doubled?

Put your pencil down. The test is over.

Andrew Brodie: More Mental Maths Tests 9–10 © A & C Black

Test 7

First name _____ Last name _____

School _____

Total marks

Practice question

Five-second questions

1		$\frac{7}{10}$

2	

3		42

4		29

5	

Ten-second questions

6		28 82

7		3.4

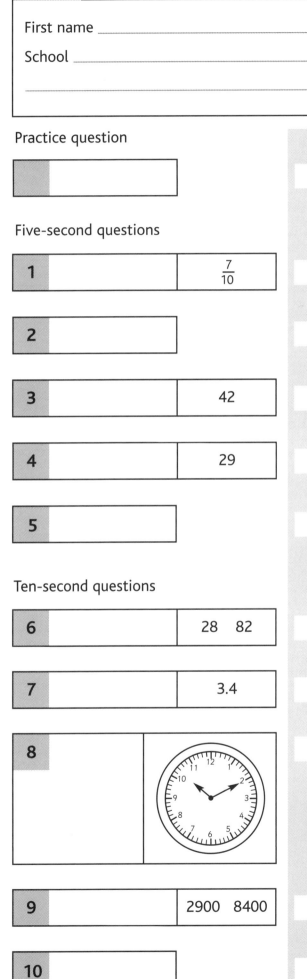

8	

9		2900 8400

10	

11		6.4

12	... 48 54 60 66		78 ...

13	£	£35

14		6.9

15	

JANUARY

Monday		5	12	19	26
Tuesday		6	13	20	27
Wednesday		7	14	21	28
Thursday	1	8	15	22	29
Friday	2	9	16	23	30
Saturday	3	10	17	24	31
Sunday	4	11	18	25	

Fifteen-second questions

16	1 2 3 4 6 8 9 12 24

17	cm²

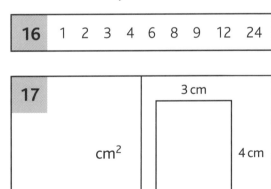

3 cm

4 cm

18	£	£1.75

19	£	£3.40

20	

Practice question

	8

Five-second questions

1	0.7	$\frac{7}{10}$

2	42

3	58	42

4	36	29

5	5

Ten-second questions

6	110	28 82

7	2.6	3.4

8	22.10	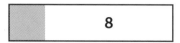

9	5500	2900 8400

10	225

11	640	6.4

12	... 48 54 60 66	**72**	78 ...

13	£7	£35

14	13.8	6.9

15	**Tuesday**

JANUARY				
Monday	5	12	19	26
Tuesday	6	13	20	27
Wednesday	7	14	21	28
Thursday	1	8	15	22	29
Friday	2	9	16	23	30
Saturday	3	10	17	24	31
Sunday	4	11	18	25

Fifteen-second questions

16	1 2 3 4 6 8 (9) 12 24

17	12 cm²	3 cm 4 cm

18	£7	£1.75

19	£16.60	£3.40

20	32

Test 8

Before playing the test on the CD give each child a copy of the test and read out the following script:

Listen to the instructions carefully. I will answer any questions that you have after I have finished reading the instructions to you. Once the test starts you will not be able to ask any questions.

The first question is a practice question. In the test there will then be twenty questions.

Each question has an answer box. Make sure that you only write the answer to the correct question in the box. Try to work out each answer in your head. You can make notes outside the answer box if this helps you but do not try to write out calculations because you will not have enough time. For some questions you will find important information already provided for you.

Each question will be read out twice. Listen carefully then work out your answer. If you cannot do the question, just put a cross. If you make a mistake, do not rub out the wrong answer; cross it out and write the correct answer.

Some questions are easy and some are more difficult. Do not worry if you find a question hard; just do your best. I hope that you enjoy the test.

At this point, answer any questions that the children ask.

Now listen carefully to the practice question. You will hear the question twice, then you will have five seconds to work out and write down the answer.

> *What is ten take away four?*

> *What is ten take away four?*

Allow the children five seconds to write the answer, then say:

Put your pencil down.

Check that the children have written the answer to the practice question in the practice question answer box. Remind them that they cannot ask any more questions once the test is started. When you are ready press start on your CD player.

When the test is finished ask the children to stop writing then collect the test sheets. For ease of marking we have created a copy of the test paper with the answers entered in the appropriate boxes.

Questions for Test 8

For each of the first ten questions you have five seconds to work out and write down the answer.

1   Write the decimal zero point two five as a fraction.

2   Eight times seven.

3   Divide four thousand by ten.

4   Add twelve to ninety-nine.

5   Subtract fourteen from thirty.

For each of the next questions you have ten seconds to work out and write down the answer.

6   Add forty-three to one hundred and eighty-one.

7   Write four and a quarter litres in millilitres.

8   Look at your answer sheet. The clock shows the time a ferry leaves one evening. Write the time using twenty-four hour clock notation.

9   Find the difference between twenty-eight and eighty-four.

10   What is half of five point four?

11   Multiply four point nine by one thousand.

12   Look at your answer sheet. Write the missing number in the sequence.

13   What is twenty percent of seventy pounds?

14   What is one hundredth of four kilograms?

15   The answer sheet shows the month of April on a page from a calendar. What day of the week was the fourth of May?

For each of the next five questions you have fifteen seconds to work out and write down the answer.

16   Subtract four point nine from nine point one.

17   Look at your answer sheet. What is the area of the rectangle?

18   How many edges does a cube have?

19   Look at your answer sheet. Draw a ring around the number that is not a factor of thirty.

20   Find half of half of sixteen.

Put your pencil down. The test is over.

Andrew Brodie: More Mental Maths Tests 9–10 © A & C Black

Test 8

First name _____ Last name _____

School _____

_____

Total marks

Practice question

Five-second questions

1		0.25

2		

3		4000

4		99

5		14

Ten-second questions

6		43 181

7	ml	$4\frac{1}{4}$ l

8		

9		28 84

10		5.4

11		4.9

12	... 25 50 75 100		150 ...

13	£		£70

14		g	4 kg

15					

APRIL					
Monday		6	13	20	27
Tuesday		7	14	21	28
Wednesday	1	8	15	22	29
Thursday	2	9	16	23	30
Friday	3	10	17	24	
Saturday	4	11	18	25	
Sunday	5	12	19	26	

Fifteen-second questions

16		4.9 9.1

17	cm^2	2.5 cm
		4 cm

18		

19	1 2 3 4 5 6 10 15 30

20		

Practice question

6

Five-second questions

1	$\frac{1}{4}$	0.25

2	56

3	400	4000

4	111	99

5	16	14

Ten-second questions

6	224	43 181

7	4250 ml	$4\frac{1}{4}$ l

8	20.35	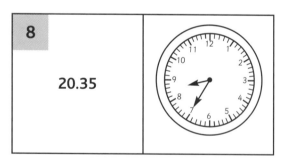

9	56	28 84

10	2.7	5.4

11	4900	4.9

12	... 25 50 75 100	125	150 ...

13	£14	£70

14	40 g	4 kg

15	**Monday**

	APRIL			
Monday	6	13	20	27
Tuesday	7	14	21	28
Wednesday	1	8	15	22	29
Thursday	2	9	16	23	30
Friday	3	10	17	24
Saturday	4	11	18	25
Sunday	5	12	19	26

Fifteen-second questions

16	4.2	4.9 9.1

17	10 cm^2	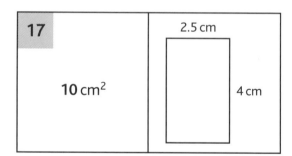

2.5 cm

4 cm

18	12

19	1 2 3 (4) 5 6 10 15 30

20	4

Test 9

Before playing the test on the CD give each child a copy of the test and read out the following script:

> **Listen to the instructions carefully. I will answer any questions that you have after I have finished reading the instructions to you. Once the test starts you will not be able to ask any questions.**
>
> **The first question is a practice question. In the test there will then be twenty questions.**
>
> **Each question has an answer box. Make sure that you only write the answer to the correct question in the box. Try to work out each answer in your head. You can make notes outside the answer box if this helps you but do not try to write out calculations because you will not have enough time. For some questions you will find important information already provided for you.**
>
> **Each question will be read out twice. Listen carefully then work out your answer. If you cannot do the question, just put a cross. If you make a mistake, do not rub out the wrong answer; cross it out and write the correct answer.**
>
> **Some questions are easy and some are more difficult. Do not worry if you find a question hard; just do your best. I hope that you enjoy the test.**

At this point, answer any questions that the children ask.

> **Now listen carefully to the practice question. You will hear the question twice, then you will have five seconds to work out and write down the answer.**
>
> > *What is twelve take away three?*
> >
> > *What is twelve take away three?*

Allow the children five seconds to write the answer, then say:

> **Put your pencil down.**

Check that the children have written the answer to the practice question in the practice question answer box. Remind them that they cannot ask any more questions once the test is started. When you are ready press start on your CD player.

When the test is finished ask the children to stop writing then collect the test sheets. For ease of marking we have created a copy of the test paper with the answers entered in the appropriate boxes.

For each of the first ten questions you have five seconds to work out and write down the answer.

1 Divide six thousand by ten.

2 Multiply seven by nine.

3 What is the difference between seventeen and forty?

4 Increase ninety by twenty.

5 What is the remainder when eleven is divided by three?

For each of the next questions you have ten seconds to work out and write down the answer.

6 What is the total of forty, fifty and sixty?

7 Eight minus two point nine.

8 Look at your answer sheet. The clock shows the time a radio programme starts one evening. Write the time using twenty-four hour clock notation.

9 Take zero point five from six point two.

10 Multiply twenty-four by four.

11 Divide six hundred and fifty by one hundred.

12 Look at your answer sheet. Write the missing number in the sequence.

13 What is five percent of forty pounds?

14 Half of five point two.

15 The answer sheet shows the month of September on a page from a calendar. What day of the week was the thirtieth of August?

For each of the next five questions you have fifteen seconds to work out and write down the answer.

16 What is the difference between seven point two and five point nine?

17 Look at your answer sheet. What is the area of the rectangle?

18 How many edges does a tetrahedron have?

19 Look at your answer sheet. Draw a ring around the number that is not a square number.

20 What is my change from one hundred pounds when I spend sixty-eight pounds forty pence?

Put your pencil down. The test is over.

First name _____ Last name _____

School _____

Total marks [____]

Practice question

[____]

Five-second questions

| 1 | | 6000 |

| 2 | | |

| 3 | | 17 |

| 4 | | 90 |

| 5 | | 11 |

Ten-second questions

| 6 | | 40 50 60 |

| 7 | | 8 2.9 |

| 8 | | 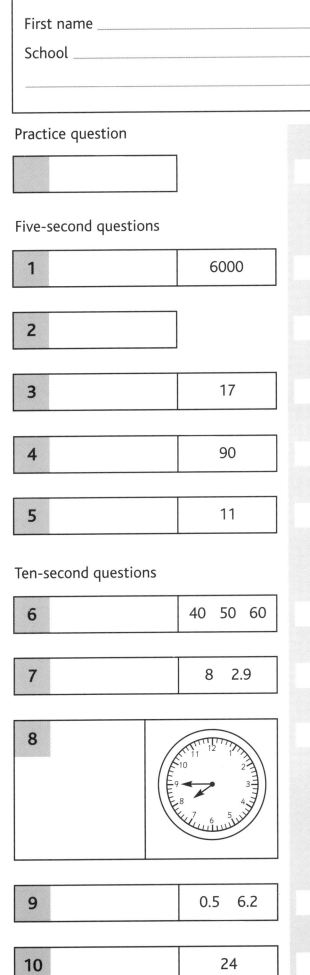 |

| 9 | | 0.5 6.2 |

| 10 | | 24 |

| 11 | | 650 |

| 12 | ... 99 103 107 111 | | 119 ... |

| 13 | £ | | £40 |

| 14 | | 5.2 |

| 15 | |

SEPTEMBER

Monday		7	14	21	28
Tuesday	1	8	15	22	29
Wednesday	2	9	16	23	30
Thursday	3	10	17	24	
Friday	4	11	18	25	
Saturday	5	12	19	26	
Sunday	6	13	20	27	

Fifteen-second questions

| 16 | | 7.2 5.9 |

| 17 | | cm² | 2.5 cm / 6 cm |

| 18 | | |

| 19 | 1 4 9 16 25 42 64 |

| 20 | £ | | £68.40 |

Practice question

	9

Five-second questions

1	**600**	6000

2	**63**

3	**23**	17

4	**110**	90

5	**2**	11

Ten-second questions

6	**150**	40 50 60

7	**5.1**	8 2.9

8	**19.45**	

9	**5.7**	0.5 6.2

10	**96**	24

11	**6.5**	650

12	... 99 103 107 111 **115**	119 ...

13	**£2**	£40

14	**2.6**	5.2

15	**Sunday**

SEPTEMBER

Monday		7	14	21	28
Tuesday	1	8	15	22	29
Wednesday	2	9	16	23	30
Thursday	3	10	17	24	
Friday	4	11	18	25	
Saturday	5	12	19	26	
Sunday	6	13	20	27	

Fifteen-second questions

16	**1.3**	7.2 5.9

17	**15** cm^2	2.5 cm 6 cm

18	**6**

19	1 4 9 16 25 (42) 64

13	**£31.60**	£68.40

Test 10

Before playing the test on the CD give each child a copy of the test and read out the following script:

> **Listen to the instructions carefully. I will answer any questions that you have after I have finished reading the instructions to you. Once the test starts you will not be able to ask any questions.**

> **The first question is a practice question. In the test there will then be twenty questions.**

> **Each question has an answer box. Make sure that you only write the answer to the correct question in the box. Try to work out each answer in your head. You can make notes outside the answer box if this helps you but do not try to write out calculations because you will not have enough time. For some questions you will find important information already provided for you.**

> **Each question will be read out twice. Listen carefully then work out your answer. If you cannot do the question, just put a cross. If you make a mistake, do not rub out the wrong answer; cross it out and write the correct answer.**

> **Some questions are easy and some are more difficult. Do not worry if you find a question hard; just do your best. I hope that you enjoy the test.**

At this point, answer any questions that the children ask.

> **Now listen carefully to the practice question. You will hear the question twice, then you will have five seconds to work out and write down the answer.**

>> *What is eight minus three?*

>> *What is eight minus three?*

Allow the children five seconds to write the answer, then say:

> **Put your pencil down.**

Check that the children have written the answer to the practice question in the practice question answer box. Remind them that they cannot ask any more questions once the test is started. When you are ready press start on your CD player.

When the test is finished ask the children to stop writing then collect the test sheets. For ease of marking we have created a copy of the test paper with the answers entered in the appropriate boxes.

Questions for Test 10

For each of the first ten questions you have five seconds to work out and write down the answer.

1 Divide eight thousand by ten.

2 Share sixty-three between nine.

3 Find the total of nineteen and seven.

4 Take twenty-three from ninety.

5 What is the remainder when sixteen is divided by seven?

For each of the next questions you have ten seconds to work out and write down the answer.

6 What is the total of sixty, seventy and eighty?

7 Four point six plus two point eight.

8 Look at your answer sheet. The clock shows the time a late evening radio programme finishes. Write the time using twenty-four hour clock notation.

9 Eight point four minus zero point six.

10 Multiply twenty-three by five.

11 Divide nine hundred and eighty by one hundred.

12 Look at your answer sheet. Write the missing number in the sequence.

13 What is five percent of sixty pounds?

14 Half of seven point six.

15 The answer sheet shows the month of October on a page from a calendar. What day of the week was the thirtieth of September?

For each of the next five questions you have fifteen seconds to work out and write down the answer.

16 What is the difference between nine point seven and six point eight?

17 Look at your answer sheet. What is the area of the rectangle?

18 Share fourteen pounds between five people.

19 Look at your answer sheet. Draw a ring around the number that is a square number.

20 What is my change from one hundred pounds when I spend thirty-seven pounds eighty pence?

Put your pencil down. The test is over.

Andrew Brodie: More Mental Maths Tests 9–10 © A & C Black

Test 10

First name _____ Last name _____

School _____

Total marks [ ]

Practice question

[ ]

Five-second questions

1		8000

2		63

3		19

4		23

5		16

Ten-second questions

6		60 70 80

7		4.6 2.8

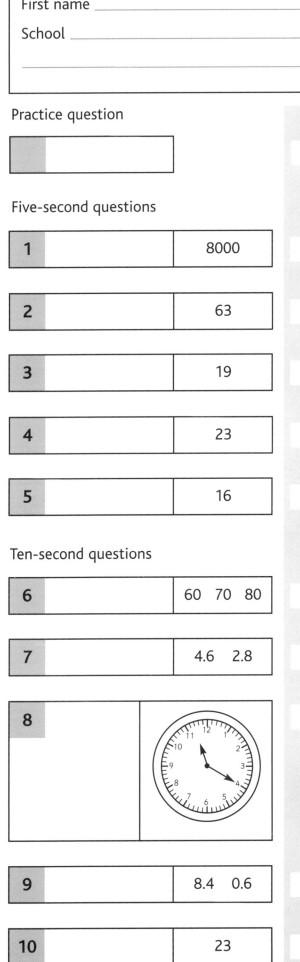

8	

9		8.4 0.6

10		23

11		980

12	... 47 44 41		35 ...

13	£	£60

14		7.6

15	

OCTOBER				
Monday	5	12	19	26
Tuesday	6	13	20	27
Wednesday	7	14	21	28
Thursday	1 8	15	22	29
Friday	2 9	16	23	30
Saturday	3 10	17	24	31
Sunday	4 11	18	25	

Fifteen-second questions

16		9.7 6.8

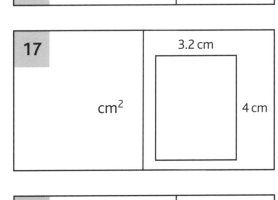

17	cm²	3.2 cm / 4 cm

18	£	£14

19	24 34 44 54 64 74 84 94

20	£	£37.80

Practice question

	5

Five-second questions

1	800	8000

2	7	63

3	26	19

4	67	23

5	2	16

Ten-second questions

6	210	60 70 80

7	7.4	4.6 2.8

8	23.20	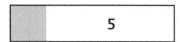

9	7.8	8.4 0.6

10	115	23

11	9.8	980

12	... 47 44 41 **38**	35 ...

13	£3	£60

14	3.8	7.6

15	Wednesday

OCTOBER				
Monday	5	12	19	26
Tuesday	6	13	20	27
Wednesday	7	14	21	28
Thursday	1	8	15	22	29
Friday	2	9	16	23	30
Saturday	3	10	17	24	31
Sunday	4	11	18	25

Fifteen-second questions

16	2.9	9.7 6.8

17	12.8 cm²	3.2 cm / 4 cm

18	£2.80	£14

19	24 34 44 54 (64) 74 84 94

20	£62.20	£37.80

Pupil record sheet

You may wish to record your pupils' scores as they complete each test.

Page 44 consists of a record sheet on which you can enter the pupils' names down the left hand column and the dates of the tests along the top. Page 45 features a graph for recording the scores for each individual pupil. By photocopying this sheet for every member of the class you can monitor each individual's progress from test to test.

It is worth observing where the pupils are making errors. Errors may occur on particular types of questions, perhaps where certain vocabulary is used. Is there a pattern to their problems?

You may also find that some pupils find the time restrictions challenging. Do they find the five-second questions more difficult, for example, simply due to the speed with which they have to answer?

Where patterns do emerge you will be able to target your teaching to address the pupils' needs. You should then find improvements as the pupils work through the set of tests.

Pupil Record Sheet

Class _____

Test number:	1	2	3	4	5	6	7	8	9	10
Date:										
Name:										

Pupil Progress Graph

Name _____

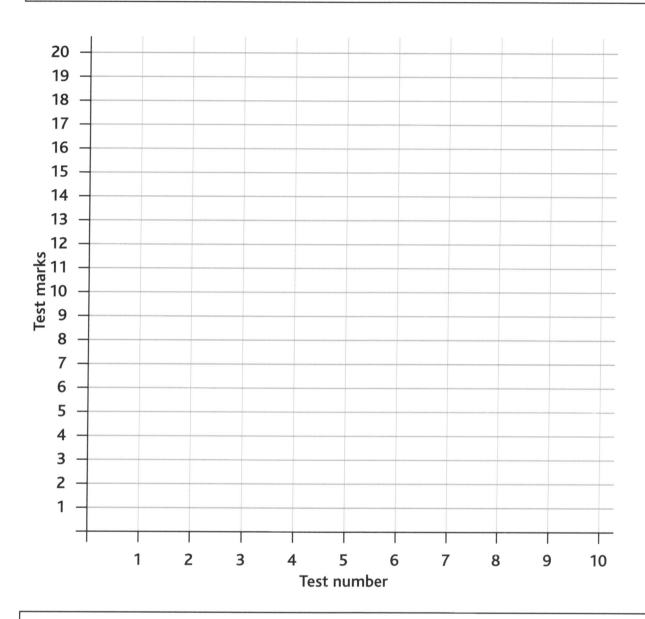

Comments, including any particular areas of difficulty

Mental Maths Puzzles

The puzzles below provide practice of addition and subtraction facts as well as of logical thinking. More puzzles like these, together with harder versions, can be found in Maths Mindstretchers for Ages 9–11.

Name _____   Date _____

Look carefully at the puzzle. It has a target number of 12.

You need to write some numbers to make a subtraction with an answer of 12 and an addition with an answer of 12.

Here are the numbers
you must use:
3 3 9 15

Now try this puzzle.
With this one you need to find
the target number as well.

Numbers to use:
4 5 8 13 17

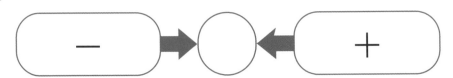

Now try this puzzle.

Numbers to use:
3 5 8 11 16

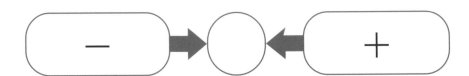

Now try this puzzle.

Numbers to use:
5 9 11 14 25

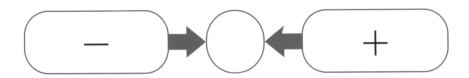

Now try this puzzle.

Numbers to use:
5 6 9 15 20

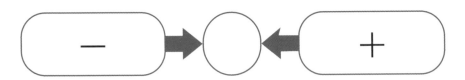

Mental Maths Puzzles

The puzzles below provide practice of addition, subtraction and multiplication facts as well as of logical thinking. More puzzles like these, together with harder versions, can be found in Maths Mindstretchers for Ages 9–11.

Name _____   Date _____

Look carefully at the puzzle. It has a target number of 32.

You need to write some numbers to make a subtraction with an answer of 32, a multiplication with an answer of 32 and an addition with an answer of 32.

Here are the numbers you must use: 3 4 5 8 27 35

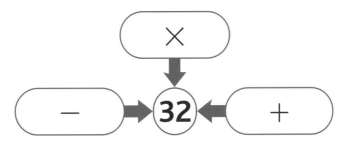

Try each of the puzzles in the same way.

Target number: 36
Numbers to use: 4 4 9 9 27 40

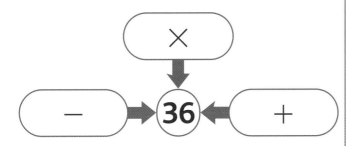

Target number: 40
Numbers to use: 60 10 8 30 5 20

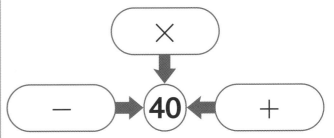

Target number: 28
Numbers to use: 9 4 36 7 19 8

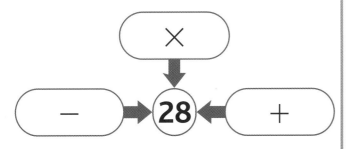

Target number: 56
Numbers to use: 34 8 24 80 7 22

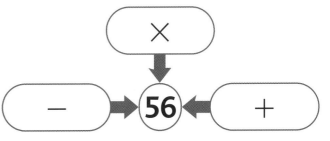

Mental Maths Puzzles

The puzzle below provides practice of addition, subtraction, multiplication and division facts as well as of logical thinking. More puzzles like these, together with harder versions, can be found in Maths Mindstretchers for Ages 9–11.

Name _____   Date _____

You need to write some numbers to make a division with an answer of 6, a subtraction with an answer of 6, an addition with an answer of 6 and a multiplication with an answer of 6.

Here are the numbers you must use: 1 2 3 3 3 5 9 18

Write them in the correct places on the puzzle.

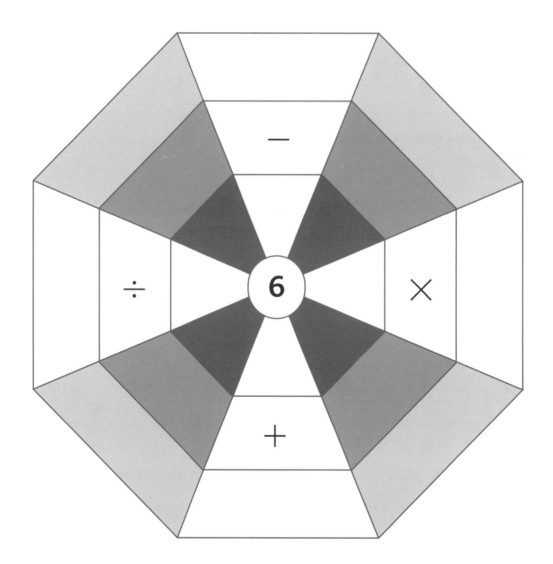

Andrew Brodie: More Mental Maths Tests 9–10 © A & C Black